CAPITALIST BEDTIME $TORIE$

STORIES THE RICH TELL THEIR CHILDREN

VOLUME 1

B. PARAISO

Cover Design by 100Covers.com
Formatted by FormattedBooks.com

ISBN: 978-1-7346715-0-6

FOR MY CHILDREN, NIDO AND JOIE,
THE GREATEST PRODUCT I EVER HAD A HAND IN CREATING.

Foreword

This book was written with the hope of passing certain values on to my children. Capitalism, as it seems in modern times, has received a negative stigma. This is especially true with today's youth. One cannot turn on the news without seeing college-age young people protesting what they view as an unjust system. How did we get here?

I believe their view has been skewed by a misunderstanding of what capitalism is. Many believe that the system takes advantage of the poor and underprivileged, that it rewards certain groups of people for previous atrocities. Nothing can be farther from the truth. From the start of civilization and our transition from being hunters and gatherers, mankind has engaged in the concept of trade. Trade is based on the underlying moral premise of value for value. It is for one's benefit, not injury, that trading is done. This is the essence of capitalism.

Capitalism is viewed as selfish, but I believe the concept of selfishness has been misconstrued. Ayn Rand, the great author and philosopher, defined selfishness as "the pursuit of one's rational self-interest." Our founding principles as a nation echo this belief in the Declaration of Independence's famous phrase "pursuit of happiness." Capitalism's purpose is to enrich, not to exploit. It is about empathy, not selfishness. One cannot become rich by solely being selfish. They can only become rich by solving other people's problems. The more numerous or larger the problems they solve, the richer they become. The system thrives on innovation and improvement. Money and wealth are created by the creation of value, not just the passing of some static resource between parties.

No other economic system has lifted more people from poverty and improved their lives as capitalism has. The purest form, *laissez-faire*, is totally free from government intervention. The government plays no role in the transactions between private parties. Although, in our own country, a variation or mixed type of economy is practiced, I believe understanding certain truths about capitalism, as a whole, will help us thrive.

My hope is that this book will help not only my children, but other people and their children understand and appreciate the benefits of the economic system that we enjoy. By understanding the foundation, there is no limit upon which we can build.

My sincere wish is that this book helps you in some way achieve your own "pursuit of happiness."

Respectfully,
B. Paraiso

Acknowledgments

I would first like to thank God. Without him, no undertaking is possible. My wife Joyce, who is the love of my life and has always driven me to improve constantly. My children, Nido and Joie, for being the inspiration and purpose of this work. I love you more than words could ever describe. My parents for the lessons that they instilled, and the love they always showed. My brothers, Bruce and Bernard, for their immeasurable support, and all my brothers and sisters worldwide in the Iglesia Ni Cristo (Church of Christ) and our executive minister, Brother Eduardo V. Manalo. His example and dynamic leadership are truly an inspiration. All glory be to God.

I would like to invite everyone to learn more about the Iglesia Ni Cristo (Church of Christ) and its message by visiting www.incmedia.org.

I want to thank the people that have entered my life at one time or another and that I have had the honor of considering my friends. There are too many to name. You know who you are. Thank you for the time you have given me, the lessons you have taught, and the love that you have shown.

To all United States Marines past and present and all United States Service Members past and present, my brothers in arms, your sacrifice is what gives us the freedom to engage in capitalism. Thank you for all that you do. To the veteran Knights that took the time to train a young prince. You know who you are. And a special thank you to the United States Marine Corps, there is no more perfect an organization in its ideals, traditions, and purpose. The lessons I learned as a United States Marine have forever shaped my life. *Semper Fidelis.*

To my literary influences, your works have truly helped to inspire me. These stories were either retold, inspired, or influenced by the following...

Thank you to Ayn Rand, Aesop, Robert Greene, Milton Friedman, Thomas Sowell, Walter Williams, Adam Smith, Robert Kiyosaki, Ray Dalio, Tony Robbins, Ben Shapiro, Yaron Brook, Larry Elder, Jordan Peterson, Tim Ferriss, Napoleon Hill, Dale Carnegie, and many more.

And finally, thank you to anyone that has taken the time to read or listen to this work.

Respectfully,
B. Paraiso

CAPITALI$T BEDTIME $TORIE$

STORIES THE RICH TELL THEIR CHILDREN

VOLUME 1

B. PARAISO

Contents

The Elephant

One day, long ago, a visiting circus had stopped to perform at a small town. A young boy, happy to see the circus, walked by the area where the animals were kept before their performances. He found a huge elephant eating grass. This creature was the biggest thing he had ever seen in his life, and he was amazed to see that this giant animal was only secured by having his foot tied to a thin rope secured to a stake in the ground.

Curious, the young boy asked the elephant keeper, "Will that thin rope really stop that elephant?"

The elephant keeper replied, "There is no way that thin rope will stop that elephant."

Confused, the young boy asked, "Why tie him with that rope if it cannot stop him?"

The elephant keeper explained, "When the elephant was very young, his foot was always tied with a thin rope. Because he was little and not very strong, the rope was effective in keeping him in one place. He would try and try to break free, but at that age, he was not strong enough to break the rope. As he grew, the rope continued to be tied to his foot. He continued to try to break it, but he was still not strong enough."

The elephant keeper concluded by saying, "Eventually, the elephant had given up trying to break the rope. He believed that the thin rope could never be broken. This is now his belief. It is his truth. So, although he could easily break free if he wanted to, he will never try."

"That is why we tie him with a rope that will not stop him."

Lessons: Limits and limitations are what you place on yourself. Children are born without limitations. Constraints must be placed on them by others. They are like new computers, free from any operating system or software. Fears, limits, entitlement belief, victim mentality, racism, hate, and other belief systems must be downloaded or taught. With continuous reinforcement, beliefs are placed on them until they become true. Why should those beliefs be limiting? Why not unleash their potential early on? Help them understand that they are the ones who set their limits by their effort.

The Businessman and His Son

In a city like any other city lived a successful Businessman and his family. His only son was still a young boy, fun-loving, and lazy. The carefree youth would spend money freely, oblivious to the cost of things, and did nothing to help around the house. The Businessman had observed throughout the years that many of his wealthy friends' children had grown up to be spoiled and entitled adults. Fearful that his son would arrive at the same fate, he set out to teach his son the value of money.

One day, he called his son before him and explained, "From today onward, you will be given your evening meal on the condition that you provide some earnings acquired by you throughout the day."

At first the boy was confused, but after seeing the seriousness in his father's face, he knew that there was no room to complain or negotiate.

The boy approached his mother and told her everything. Being the nurturing, loving, mother she was, she did not want her only child to get in trouble or miss a meal. She reached into her purse and gave him a gold coin.

At the dinner table the next night, the Businessman asked his son about his earnings for the day. The boy promptly presented him with the gold coin. Upon seeing the gold coin, and knowing the value of it, the man knew his son didn't earn the money. He asked his son to throw the gold coin into the storm drain located by the front of the courtyard. Without hesitation, the boy did as his father asked. He tossed the gold coin into the drain without a moment's thought. He then came back inside and had his evening meal.

Early the next morning, the Businessman sent his wife out of town to visit her parents. When the boy awoke, the Businessman reminded his son about the conditions for receiving his evening meal. He also informed him that his mother had left for a few days to visit her parents.

With the knowledge that his mother was not there to give him money, the boy approached his grandfather. The grandfather, who very much loved his only grandchild, would do anything for him. The boy asked his grandfather for money. The old man, without hesitation, reached into his pocket and gave the boy a gold coin.

Later that evening at the dinner table, the Businessman asked his son about his earnings for the day. The boy promptly presented him with the gold coin. Upon seeing the gold coin, the father, once again, knew that he didn't earn the money. He asked his son to throw the gold coin into the drain. Once again, without hesitation, the boy did as his father asked. He tossed the gold coin into the drain without a moment's thought. He then came back inside and had his evening meal.

After putting his son to bed, the Businessman called his father and told him about the lesson he was trying to impart unto his grandson. The grandfather understood completely. He told his son, the Businessman, that he would make himself scarce for the next few days.

The next morning, the Businessman again reminded his young son about the conditions for his evening meal. The boy went looking for his grandfather, but he was nowhere to be found. With no one else he could ask to give him money, the boy had no choice but to go to the market and look for work.

The young boy went from shop to shop, stall to stall, but to no avail. He could not find any work. Eventually, after some time, he was able to find a shopkeeper who agreed to give him some work.

The shopkeeper told him he would pay him one piece of silver if he were to carry his trunk all the way back to his home. The boy had no choice but to agree to the deal. A few hours later, the boy had completed the task and received his payment, but he was drenched in sweat. The trunk was not the heaviest, but the terrain and distance were not as easy as the young boy had anticipated. The boy's neck and back ached, and his feet were sore. Callouses started to form on his hands. Never had he experienced this type of exhaustion.

That evening, at the table, before dinner, the father asked his son about his earnings for the day. The boy reluctantly presented him his one piece of silver. He knew his father would tell him to throw it down the drain. The young boy could not imagine just throwing away his hard-earned money. The Businessman, as he had done the previous evenings, asked his young son to throw his one piece of silver into the storm drain as the condition for his evening meal.

The young boy, with tears in his eyes, refused.

"Father," he said, "My entire body is aching. I have calloused my hands. My feet are sore, my back and my neck ache. All this to earn my one piece of silver. Now you want me to just throw it down the drain?"

Upon hearing this, the Businessman knew that his young son had learned the lesson. The boy was taking his first steps towards responsibility and adulthood. The father, beaming with pride, proudly said to his son, "Put it in your pocket. You have earned it. It is yours."

Lessons: The value of something is based on what you trade for it. The young boy did not value the gold coins that he received from his mother

and grandfather. He did not feel a sense of loss when they were wasted because he did not earn them. There was nothing traded by him to obtain those gold coins. Once his earned silver coin was to be wasted, he understood the value. Although the silver is less valuable than gold. The silver coin, earned by his own effort, was more valuable to him than the previously wasted gold coins.

There is a certain dignity that comes with work. There is a feeling of self-pride that comes with paying your own way. The power you feel by determining your own life. It illustrates the difference between two opposing belief systems: Self-reliance versus Entitlement. One is a belief system based on self-reliance and self-determination. The other is a belief system based on entitlement and what you feel is other people's obligation to you.

Self-reliance is about earning. Entitlement is about deserving. If you earn something, you never have to say that you deserve it.

Entitlement exists on the axiom that because I am alive, therefore a certain quality of life needs to be provided. The entitlement belief often creates a feeling of resentment. The beneficiary resents the benefactor, meaning the one who receives resents the one who gives. That is why there is an adage that says, "gratuity is a guilt". The feeling of obligation or the feeling of reliance on others is poison to one's soul. It reduces the feeling of self-worth and often leads to feelings of unhappiness.

The self-reliance belief has the opposite effect. Self-reliance and self-determination create pride and confidence in one's ability that raises one's feeling of self-worth and often leads to feelings of happiness. Happiness is obtained by the overcoming of obstacles in the pursuit of the realization of one's goals.

Which belief system do you want to follow?

The Grasshopper and the Ant

O n a field like any other field lived a Grasshopper and an Ant. The Grasshopper was carefree by nature. He spent his time hopping along, singing his songs, and basking in the sun. The Ant, conversely, was very diligent. He often spent his time foraging for food, fixing his home, and generally trying to improve his life.

One summer day, the two happened to cross paths. The Grasshopper was sunbathing on a rock. The Ant was on his daily routine of bringing food back to his home. The Grasshopper asked, "What are you doing?" To which the Ant replied, "I am storing extra food and supplies in my home. One never knows when you may need it. I believe it is better to have and not need than to need and not have." The Grasshopper chided him, "That is the most ridiculous thing I have ever heard. Look around you. We live in a time of abundance. Food is everywhere. You barely need to exert any effort, and you will find all you need. Why not be like me and enjoy your life? You are letting the best of life pass you by." The Ant, unperturbed by his comments, thanked the Grasshopper for the conversation and went on his way.

This continued all the days of the summer and into the fall. The Ant would diligently bring supplies back to his home, and the Grasshopper would tease the Ant, criticizing him and telling him he was wasting his time. The Ant paid him no mind. He maintained his course of action. He knew in his heart that it was the right thing to do regardless of what others believed.

Then one day, winter came suddenly. A blizzard set in and blanketed everything in deep snow. The Grasshopper tried and tried but could not find food. The time of abundance had ceased. Only scarcity now prevailed. The Ant, secure with his provisions, lived comfortably in his home until the coming of the spring. The Grasshopper eventually succumbed to the scarcity and perished, thus ending his carefree life.

Lessons: Times of economic abundance are just like the seasons. They come in cycles. It is prudent to save in times of plenty, for one never knows when a season of scarcity will arrive. At least ten percent of one's income should be consistently dedicated to savings. In times of abundance, this percentage should increase. The benefit of saving is that it provides peace of mind to the saver; they know that they have the reserves to weather whatever storms life may bring. And should the need not arise, these reserves can be used for investment capital, providing a greater cushion to the investor once it reaps the Return On Investment (ROI). This peace of mind is what truly brings a carefree life.

The Crows

One day, two Crows were flying over the desert and dying of thirst. They happened across two pitchers that had some water left in them. However, the pitchers were very big. The Crows tried and tried but could not get to the water.

The first Crow took a few moments to think, then he decided to act. He picked up a stone and dropped it into the pitcher. He picked up another and another. Slowly but surely, the water level rose.

The second crow seeing this, imitated the first crow. He picked up stones and dropped them into his pitcher. However, after seeing how long it was taking, decided to give up and fly away to seek water elsewhere.

The first Crow maintained his course of dropping stones until he could drink from the pitcher. He was able to quench his thirst and save his life.

The second Crow searched and searched but was unable to find water anywhere and eventually succumbed to his thirst and perished.

Lessons: Success is the sum of small actions repeated over time. Diligence and discipline are essential elements in achieving any worthwhile goal including financial goals. Many people often become discouraged because they seek immediate gratification for their efforts. They seek the get rich quick solution, they do not understand that building true wealth takes time. They give up early before their efforts can produce results. Success and financial success are like a plant that requires consistent watering and nurturing. Only from consistency can your efforts sprout and bear the fruits of success.

The Hoarder

In a small village like any other village, lived an old Hoarder. This Hoarder never spent any of his gold. He would only hoard his gold coins and keep them in a large bag buried at the base of an old tree in his backyard. Every day he would dig up the bag and look at all his gold coins. After looking at the gold coins, he would seal the bag and bury it again at the base of the tree. He did this daily without fail.

One day, a thief happened by and noticed the old Hoarder's routine. Later that night, the thief returned, dug up the bag, and stole it.

The next day, the Hoarder, following his regular routine, went to dig up the bag. When he realized that it had been taken, the Hoarder was shocked and let out a scream. The Hoarder's neighbor heard the scream and hurried over. "What happened?" asked the neighbor. "It's gone. It's all gone," cried the Hoarder. "What's gone?" questioned the neighbor. "My gold. I kept it here in a bag buried at the base of this tree. I would dig it up every day and look at it, then I would bury it again," said the Hoarder. "Is that all you did with the gold?" asked the neighbor. "Yes," replied the Hoarder. "Then why don't you just fill a bag with stones and pretend it is gold?" suggested the neighbor. "It would serve the same exact purpose."

Lessons: Money not in circulation has no benefit. It is not being suggested that one should not save. Saving money is one essential step in wealth accumulation. Saving, however, is not the only step.

Once one has saved or accumulated capital, this capital needs to be invested to generate a return. The reason for this is that the purchasing power of that money is diminished by something known as "inflation." Inflation is the rising costs of goods and the decreased purchasing power of money. The average rate is about three percent per year. This means that your money must grow at a rate higher than three percent per year for you to purchase the same amount of goods later.

Money is only a tool, a means of exchange. It is only an illusion. The dollars we use have no real value; they are not backed by any hard asset such as gold. They are only pieces of paper we assign a value to. These pieces of paper are issued by our quasi-central bank known as the "Federal Reserve." That is why our dollars are known as Federal Reserve Notes. We operate on what is known as a "fiat" system, or by government decree. This means the currency we use has the value of whatever the government says it is. Our monetary system is only backed by debt.

Our banking system uses something known as "fractional reserve banking." This means that for every dollar that a commercial bank deposits into the Federal Reserve, it can draw up to nine dollars, which it can then loan out. It is only required to keep a portion or fraction of its money in reserve. The amount required by the Federal Reserve varies on the bank's assets. Banks with less than $15.2 million in assets are not required to hold reserves. Banks with $15.2 million to $110.2 million in assets have a three percent requirement. And banks with assets over $110.2 million are required to keep ten percent in reserve.

The amount or percentage kept in reserve by commercial banks can vary depending on the Federal Reserve's current policy. The Federal Reserve uses these requirements as tools to expand or constrict the economy. By lessening the requirements, more capital or money is circulated into the economy. By increasing the requirements, money or capital is taken out of circulation in the economy.

The purpose of this fractional reserve banking system is to provide more money to be used in the monetary supply. By providing more supply, we can purchase future productive effort before it is created. This, however, creates debt. Understanding the proper utilization of debt is an essential skill that must be mastered to accumulate wealth. Money must circulate for the entire system to run. It does not, however, create more money.

Money is created by the creation of value, like wood being made into a table or petroleum being converted into gasoline. Although the raw resource of wood and petroleum holds a certain value, more value was created when that raw resource was turned into something else.

The Tale of Two Villages

ong ago, in a land far away, existed two villages separated by a river and surrounded by forested mountains. Both villages consisted of farmers and their families. Life was simple for both villages. The land provided the villagers with what they needed. They grew crops and raised animals to sustain themselves. The only main difference between the two villages were their attitudes towards the other people in their community. One village had people who were friendly and always greeted each other. They often shared information and interacted with one another. The other village's people were more introverted and kept to themselves. They lived around each other but not with each other. One village became known as the Friendlies, the other village became known as the Not So Friendlies.

With the custom of sharing information, the Friendlies realized that many of the problems they faced were the same as their fellow villagers. In their free time, many villagers worked to try and solve these problems as their hobbies. A few of these problems were: how to raise more livestock, how to raise more crops, how to catch more fish, how to better cut down trees, how to build stronger homes, how to make better tasting food, and so on. The Friendlies' hobby pursuits help to develop their skills, create new tools, and develop new technology. Their skills developed into specialties, with some villagers becoming extremely proficient at certain tasks. Some villagers became so proficient that they were able to produce surpluses or extra of certain things. These included livestock, crops, fish, wood, bricks, shoes, fabrics, bread, and all kinds of new things.

This new abundance helped to create their custom of trading. At first, they traded these extras to get other things that they needed. For example, one villager would trade a sheep for a basket of fish, or a wagon full of bricks for some fabric or clothes, or shoes for a few loaves of bread, or a basket of vegetables for candles. The Friendlies came to realize a few things: the harder to produce something, the more valuable it was. The rarity of the product raised its value. More things needed to be traded to acquire it. Lastly, not everyone that wanted to trade with someone had something that the other person needed or wanted.

They decided to develop a medium for exchange. This medium had to be able to serve a few basic functions: it had to be durable, portable, identical, divisible (able to make change), and had to maintain its value. The Friendlies settled on using gold. This precious metal served all the functions that this medium needed to provide and was naturally limited by nature because the gold that was mined was in short supply. This new medium they created was called money.

The creation of money helped to ease trading and increased the amount of trading that was done. The Friendlies realized that focusing on a specialty was more productive than trying to do everything themselves as they had previously done before. The emergence of trade and money meant that they could trade their most productive efforts for the productive efforts of others and enjoy all things that they needed or wanted.

Many Friendlies decided to give up farming and raising livestock to focus on other specialties. They decided to leave the farming and livestock raising to the villagers that were more specialized in those skills. Over time, the

Friendlies grew into a bustling city where you could get everything that you needed. The Not So Friendlies kept their isolationist customs and remained farmers, maintaining their way of life, and trying to do everything individually. Their lives remained stagnant and remained as it always had.

Lessons: Money is nothing more than a means of exchange, a tool to be utilized. There should be no emotional connection attached to it.

Price or value of goods, products, and services are based on a few factors:

- **The supply of the good, product, or service.**
- **The demand of the good, product, or service.**
- **The perceived utility of the good, product or service.**

When individuals or groups focus their productive energy on activities that they are the most productive in, compared to trying to do everything themselves, it creates something known as "comparative advantage". This comparative advantage helps to increase productivity and therefore grows the economy long term.

Long term economic growth or increases in the Gross Domestic Product (GDP) is based on increases in production (goods, products, and services). It is not grown by increasing the monetary supply. An increase in the monetary supply will only stimulate more consumption in the short-term debt cycle but will invariably lead to inflation. This is because money, like any other good is controlled by the interactions between supply and demand.

The Oak Tree

In the heart of the great forest stood an old oak tree, strong and majestic. This oak tree was no different from any other oak tree in the great forest, except for its inhabitants. In the tree lived two families, one of pigs and one of eagles. The pigs had made their home at the root of the tree, while the eagles' home rested on the top. They lived in peace for many seasons.

One day, a cat happened to come across the tree and noticed the two families' living arrangement. He thought to himself, "There must be an opportunity here." He first approached the mother pig while she was foraging in the forest. "Good afternoon," he said. "I feel that I must warn you, I was walking by your oak tree and heard the mother eagle telling her chicks that soon they would be eating plump piglets for dinner. I believe she has evil intentions for your children." The mother pig thanked the cat for warning her of the danger and hurried home to protect her children.

The next day, the cat came across the mother eagle perched on a branch in the forest. "Good afternoon," he said. "I feel that I must warn you, I happened to be walking by your oak tree and heard the mother pig telling her piglets that they shouldn't worry about any eagles, for she has been digging around the oak tree roots for some time now and soon the tree will fall and kill any chicks that will grow up to become a threat to them. I believe she has evil intentions for your children." The mother eagle thanked the cat for warning her of the danger and hurried home to protect her children.

Now both mothers stayed at home with their children, fearful of what the other family would do to them in her absence. Days and then weeks passed with both families afraid to leave their home. Neither mother ventured out for food. Eventually, both families succumbed to starvation and perished. The cat, always watching from a distance, now came in and devoured both families.

Lessons: Beware of whose advice you heed and where you get your information. Many times, the information we receive is clouded by other people's intentions. Facts should be verified, considered, and then acted upon. When it comes to financial advice, seek what is known as a fiduciary.

A fiduciary is bound legally and ethically to act in your best financial interests and receives a fee. A broker comparatively is compensated by commissions for sales generated. This is the main difference between the two, their motivations.

Brokers such as: Stockbrokers, Real Estate Brokers, Mortgage Brokers, and other types, are incentivized to sell you for their commission, a fiduciary is not. It should not be misinterpreted that brokers should not be trusted. It is only prudent to understand another party's motivations if you are dealing with them.

The Democratic Wolves

O nce upon a time in a land far, far away, there was a place known as the Great Pasture. The Great Pasture was a vast grassland abundant with grass, trees, shrubs, and numerous ponds and streams. These waterways all led to the Great River. The Great River divided the two lands: the Great Pasture and the Great Forest. There was only one place to cross between the two domains, a natural rock bridge that went over the river.

As the legend goes, the Great Pasture was originally a part of the Great Forest. Until one day, lightning struck a tree and started a small fire. No one knows exactly who or what type of animal had knocked over the burning tree. What we do know is, that piece of burning tree became the spark that ignited the great fire. The great fire consumed the forest so quickly that no animal had ever seen anything like it before. The only thing that prevented the entire Great Forest from burning was the natural divide, the Great River.

The fire finally subsided, but the land was left a vast and barren wasteland. Ash and soot covered everything. After a few years passed, grasses sprung up.

The ash and soot, being natural fertilizers, transformed the wasteland into an abundant grassland. A great multitude of the animals that fed on grass, or prey animals as they were known, flocked to the Great Pasture to take advantage of the abundance. The wolves, or predators as they were known, stayed in the Great Forest because the terrain provided a better advantage for hunting.

This is how things remained for many generations: most of the prey on one side of the river, and most of the predators on the other. During this time, the two groups developed their own cultures, languages, and systems of governance.

On the predator side, the wolves' culture developed into a dominance, or need-based system. Their system meant that the dominant pack controlled the resources and distributed them according to their need. The dominant pack enjoyed certain advantages and often punished or exploited the subordinated packs.

Fighting was always taking place. One pack (or more) battled the others to assume control of the Great Forest and its abundant resources. The "alpha" of the group decided distribution based on relationships, favoritism, and political favors. There were no individual property rights. Prey animal rights were not recognized, and they were treated as such. They were considered prey. If the pack wanted something, it was theirs. Might made right, and force was the final arbiter of disputes.

The prey animals, comparatively, developed a totally different system. The fact that there were so many types of prey animals—sheep, goats, cows, chickens, ducks, geese, pigs, deer, moose, elk, and beavers—meant they needed to find common ground for all of them to live in peace. All these different prey animals had their own distinct cultures, natures, and belief systems. They decided on a representative republic.

A representative republic was a system in which a group of animals in an area elected a representative to be part of a governing body. This governing body voted on certain matters, and the resulting majority vote would become the policy for the Great Pasture. This group of representatives, or governing body, became known as the Animal Assembly.

Every animal voted for his or her representative. The representative would be accountable to the animals that elected them, and ideally would vote for, or act on, their behalf. The number of representatives in the Animal Assembly was based on the population. One representative represented every hundred-thousand animals.

The Founding Animal Assembly (or Founding Animals, as they came to be known) agreed on a couple of distinct principles that became the fundamental basis for their society:

> Each animal had the right to pursue their own individual interest, on the condition that it did not infringe on the rights of any other animal.
>
> Each animal had the right to their own individual property. No other animal could take what was yours without your permission. An unbiased court system would be provided to settle disputes.

With these principles in place, the prey animal society began to thrive. Different industries sprang up due to the animals being free to pursue their own interest. Some animals made goods, some provided services, and everyone prospered free from any intervention. The Industrial Evolution (as it was called) attracted many more prey animals from the Great Forest due to all the abundance provided by the system the Great Pasture had created.

The sheep's language became the common language, due to the sheep being the most numerous at the founding of the Great Pasture. No formal vote was ever cast at the Animal Assembly regarding the common language: Sheep. But Sheep became the language used for all matters of trade, court dealings, and government. All animals were free to speak whatever language they traditionally spoke. Many often did in their own individual private affairs, but Sheep became the language of common usage.

The Great Pasture enjoyed great prosperity and peace for a long time. Disputes between animal types, groups, and individuals still occurred, as they will always do, but for the most part, all the animals enjoyed living in the Great Pasture.

Over time, certain things started to change in their society—small at first, and then greater over time. The Animal Assembly passed certain policies that seemed to violate their founding principles.

With the growing population and need for infrastructure, the Animal Assembly passed a policy that would require each animal to provide a certain amount of labor and supplies: grass, sticks, rocks, branches, and so on, for the different projects and programs that were being commissioned by the Animal Assembly.

They called this policy a progressive tax. This meant that if you were a more productive animal, you had to provide a bigger percentage of the labor or supplies. A few animals protested, but most just accepted the change as the price to pay for living in the Great Pasture. Many animals were often heard saying, "What are you going to do? Move to the Great Forest?"

Another policy enacted by the Animal Assembly was the creation of a social safety net or welfare system. Many of the supplies collected by the taxes were used to feed and create housing for less fortunate animals. These animals were previously cared for and assisted by private charities in their local communities.

Since the time of the Great Pasture's founding, animals would group together to help these less-fortunate animals and provide the resources to assist them. Now that the Animal Assembly enacted the policy, fewer animals participated in the local charities. The main difference between the two approaches was that local charities often encouraged and helped the less fortunate animals to become independent and not require assistance. They did not have the resources to continually provide for these animals. The policy of the Animal Assembly provided assistance without stipulations of ever achieving independence. Some say this was done to secure votes for certain representatives.

The other change that occurred was the length of time that representatives were staying on the Animal Assembly. At the founding of the Great Pasture, time served as a representative was considered a civil service, not a career. The elected animals would normally only serve one or two terms then return to private life working amongst the other animals in the community. As time passed, more and more animals were becoming career representatives. These animals were nicknamed "RINOs" or Representatives in Name Only. RINOs were accused of being more interested in getting votes to stay in office than properly representing their constituents.

Although changes were taking place, general prosperity continued to be enjoyed by the animals of the Great Pasture. One day, a large group of wolves crossed over the rock bridge and into the Great Pasture. They were seeking asylum because of a war that was raging in the Great Forest. This war was known as the War of the Wolves.

There was never a formal policy controlling the immigration of animals from the Great Forest. There was never any need for one. Animals of all types constantly immigrated over, but never in any great number or frequency to be considered a problem. Any animal was free to join the Great Pasture. They just had to be documented so they could be registered to vote for representatives. Many wolves already lived in the Great Pasture. They had lived in the Great Pasture since the founding. They participated in every aspect of society and took part in the Great Pasture's system of a representative republic.

Although wolves naturally consumed other animals to sustain themselves, it was never a problem due to it being considered a natural part of life. The Great Pasture wolves would consume only the weakest of the herds and never consumed so much that it affected the other animals.

The Animal Assembly debated for some length on what to do with the wolves seeking asylum. One representative stated, "If we accept them, then we will have to provide for them. They will draw on our resources without ever having contributed!"

"You are being insensitive," denounced another representative. "We are an abundant society, and we have compassion for other animals. Shame on you. You are treating them differently because they are predators." He appealed to the Animal Assembly's emotions. The Animal Assembly narrowly voted to allow the wolves' asylum.

Asylum was awarded to the wolves, and housing and food were provided as well. For predators that were beneficiaries of the social safety net, meat was procured in two ways: a meat tax paid by the existing Great Pasture wolves and resources traded for meat to Great Pasture wolves or their companies.

The asylum wolves were happy to live in the Great Pasture. They enjoyed a better quality of life than they ever experienced in the Great Forest. Everything they needed was provided to them by the Animal Assembly. They just needed to remember to vote for RINOs that were sympathetic to their plight. It became politically detrimental to be viewed as insensitive to the needs of less fortunate animals. Any representative that questioned or suggested reform was often not reelected.

As if overnight, more and more large groups of wolves immigrated to the Great Pasture seeking asylum. They had heard of the benefits that the previous groups enjoyed and wanted a better life as well. Communities were being built to house these large groups of wolves. The difference between these communities was that Wolf was the common language being used and not Sheep. It seemed that these wolves did not want to assimilate to the existing culture of the Great Pasture but wanted to keep their own from the Great Forest. Many of these wolves reasoned, "The Great Pasture was just part of the Great Forest before some sheep burned it down. Wolf was the original language spoken here." Packs formed to assert control over these communities. The wolves in these communities often became hostile towards outsiders.

With the growing population of wolves, more wolves and animals sympathetic to wolves were elected as representatives to the Animal Assembly. The need for resources provided by taxes grew and grew. The progressive tax rates were increased to compensate. The number of less-than-fortunate animals and beneficiaries of the social safety net increased dramatically as well. And the demand for meat greatly increased.

Meat was a difficult resource to procure. It required that a prey animal's life be taken to provide it. Traditionally, the Great Pasture wolves hunted the weakest animals of the herd. The limited excess meat that these wolves accumulated was paid in tax or traded for other resources. For as long as anyone could remember, this balance could be maintained. But, because of the population change and the sudden increase of predators, meat prices increased astronomically. A solution needed to be provided.

A recently elected representative, a wolf by chance, proposed a policy that would be known as the "Circle of Life Doctrine." This policy proposed that prey animals that were weak, sick, lame, disabled, or convicted of a serious crime be sacrificed to provide for the needs of others. The policy reasoned, "When predators die, they become the grass, prey animals eat the grass, predators consume prey animals. We all support each other."

The Animal Assembly, which now mostly consisted of wolves and RINOs elected by wolves, voted to pass the proposal and the "Circle of Life Doctrine" became policy.

When the policy began its implementation, the number of animals receiving benefits from the social safety net was nearly half the population of the Great Pasture. Only half the animals living in the Great Pasture contributed to the progressive tax system.

The essence of the Great Pasture had changed greatly from what it had originally been. Personal liberty, the condition of not infringing on another animal's rights, had been violated. Personal property rights and ownership of the products of individual labor had been violated in the name of providing for another less fortunate animal's need. The ideal of the individual had now become the ideal of the collective.

The principles that once made the Great Pasture what it had been, eroded away. The new system of collectivism was just a variation of the dominance or need-based system.

The Great Pasture had become the Great Forest.

Lessons: Individuals will always vote and try to influence others to vote for what is beneficial to their own self-interest. Politicians that distribute from the treasury will always be popular with the recipients of that which is distributed. The decline of previous civilizations, like the Roman Empire, has been partially attributed to this practice.

The spending of another's money (tax spending) will never be efficient. The distributors have no stake in the matter and experience no loss if plans don't work. Special interest groups will always seek to cultivate favors if politicians can distribute those favors. This is Crony Capitalism and not true Capitalism.

Career politicians are motivated to be reelected, not to adhere to principles. Accountability for their performance is necessary. Politicians should be responsive to their constituents but exercise their own judgment guided by their principles. Ideally, they should be elected for their stated principles and record of sound judgment, not their popularity.

Open immigration cannot flourish in a welfare state. Immigrants will always come, incentivized by the possibility of receiving the benefits of a system to which they did not contribute. The flow of immigration will never stop; however, the resources required to provide for them are finite. A choice between the two must be made. The two cannot exist together.

Homogeneous societies (societies of people of the same origin) are united by a common culture, language, and cultural norms developed over an extended period. Heterogeneous societies (societies of people of various origins) must be united by a created common culture and language. Assimilation to the existing dominant culture must be done by newcomers to preserve the created dominant culture. If newcomers to society fail to assimilate, the existing dominant culture will change completely. A nation is united by its culture, language, and belief systems.

A politician's responsibility should be to their existing constituents (citizens), not new possible constituents (immigrants). Considerations should be made to contributors before they are made to recipients. If not, contributors will diminish and recipients will increase.

Personal liberties cannot be violated for the sake of others. No one is obligated to another unless they choose to be, and individual property rights cannot be violated for the sake of another's need.

Individuals are motivated to produce by selfishness (individual rational self-interest). If the ownership of their productive effort is compromised, their motivation to produce is reduced. Innovation and improvement will cease. The economy will stagnate due to no additional value (productivity and innovation) being created.

The Police Chief

In a once-small city, the population had grown rapidly and traffic was becoming a problem. The main highway connected all the major roads and served as a thoroughfare for nonresidents passing through the city. It had no posted speed limit and had a constant stream of fast-moving vehicles. Car accidents became a regular occurrence.

The mayor and city council decided that a speed limit should be set to help reduce the speed, minimize accidents, and generate revenue for the city by citing tickets. They soon began their campaign: signs were posted, billboards were erected, newspaper announcements were placed, and TV and radio commercials announced the change regularly. The day arrived, and the speed limit was enacted.

Although the purpose of the law was well-intended, no driver behavior changed. People still drove at high speeds. Accidents still occurred. Tickets were issued, but the small police force was not equipped to deal with the amount of traffic that passed through the highway. All seemed hopeless, and the people seemed set in their ways.

Surprisingly, nine months later, everything changed. The number of accidents reduced dramatically. The number of tickets being issued reduced noticeably as well. It seemed that everyone was adhering to the new law. What was causing the change?

The police chief, curious about this development, decided to investigate. He took his radar gun with him to see for himself whether people were really following the new speed limit or his officers were just being relaxed in their enforcement. He set up at the busiest part of the highway and started monitoring the vehicle speeds.

To his surprise, vehicles were adhering to the posted speed limit. Perplexed, the police chief drove to the edge of the city limits and drove the length of the highway to the end of the city.

Just outside the city limits, the chief noticed a young boy with a cardboard sign that read, "Speed trap ahead." At the other end of the city limits sat a second young boy with a sign that read "Tips." Next to him was a big container filled with money.

Lessons: You cannot legislate morality. The intent of a law cannot guarantee its compliance and effectiveness. There are laws that outlaw murder, robbery, and drugs, yet violations still occur. Although something is outlawed, compliance with the law is not guaranteed.

People are driven by incentives and benefits. Motivation by risks and punishments are not as effective. Adherence, if any, is often directly related to the severity of the punishment.

Three Little Pig Construction and Property Management

In the town of New Pork, lived three little pig brothers. These three little pigs were hardworking and diligent. All three found work in the construction industry. After a few years and after learning the different aspects of the industry, they combined the money that each had saved and started their own construction company.

Their company, known as "Three Little Pig Construction and Property Management," started small. They first constructed affordable housing made of straw. Straw was a cheaper, more cost-effective material compared to other building materials, but it was not the most durable material available in the market. The company constructed many single-story straw houses and was soon renting out the homes to many tenants. The company prided itself on being able to provide quality housing at a marketable price.

As their company grew, the company was able to develop different building techniques and incorporated a new building material into their designs: sticks. Sticks were more expensive compared to straw but were a stronger material that could support more weight. The company built multilevel apartment complexes made of sticks. These complexes could house more tenants in the same size space than the previously constructed single-story straw houses. The company soon upgraded its existing single-story straw houses to multilevel stick apartment complexes. The undertaking was a sizeable expense, but it would be well worth the investment over the long term. The company was growing to become one of the largest providers of housing in the city. Everything was going well for the three little pigs and their company until, one day, it all changed.

The mayor and city council for New Pork passed a new policy called rent control. Rent control is a form of price control that limits the amount a property owner can charge for renting out a home, or an apartment. Rent control acts as a price ceiling. It prevents rents from being charged above a certain level or increasing at a higher rate than a predetermined percentage. The law intended to provide affordable housing to the masses and to ease the housing shortage the city was experiencing.

The local newspaper, The *New Pork Swines*, sent a reporter to the company for a comment for their reaction piece. The company stated:

> *With the passing of the new rent control law, we have had to make certain changes to our business model to maintain viability. We will no longer be constructing multilevel stick apartment complexes. Our company will focus on building luxury condominium units made of brick. These luxury brick units do not fall under the scope of the new law and have no restrictions placed upon them.*
>
> *Furthermore, we will cease upgrades to our current inventory of straw houses. We will no longer be converting these single-story straw houses to multilevel stick apartment complexes. We are also in the process of selling our inventory of single-story straw houses to willing buyers. Please feel free to contact us regarding the purchase of our existing inventory.*

Lessons: Laws must not be judged by their intentions but by their outcome. There can be unintended consequences that result from the noblest of intentions.

Rent control only hurts those who it intends to help. By creating a market distortion, or false price set by the government, it significantly reduces the incentive for property owners to upgrade and builders to produce.

When upgrades to existing units become unprofitable due to the restriction on raising rents, maintenance to existing units will be kept to the minimum required by law due to the increased demand for the limited supply. There will always be renters seeking housing, but rent control takes away the incentive to keep them happy and wanting to stay in the property.

New construction will slow, and new developments will focus on markets not regulated by rent control, such as the rich. The supply of housing will be reduced. Existing stock will not be optimized due to renters not being motivated by the price to maximize utility. One example is a renter taking on roommates. If the rent is artificially low due to rates set by the government, a renter will not be incentivized to spread load costs by having roommates.

What Robin Hood Misunderstood

One sunny day in Sherwood Forest, Robin Hood and his merry band waited eagerly by the road for the next passing carriage. Soon, a carriage drawn by two horses made its way down the road. Inside the carriage was an old merchant. As the carriage came within range, Robin Hood and his men sprang from their trap and stopped the carriage.

"Good day to you sir, I am Robin Hood, and this is my band of merry men. We will be placing a toll on you for passing through our road. Seeing that you are rich, it is only fair that you pay your fair share and that it goes to the less fortunate," proclaimed Robin Hood.

"I see," said the old merchant. "I have heard of you. I pray, before I pay your toll, may we enter into a discourse?"

"I don't see why not," laughed Robin Hood.

"I am curious as to your motivations," said the merchant. "What do you hope to achieve?"

"Well, I am righting society's wrongs," replied Robin Hood smugly. "I am a warrior for a just society. I take from the rich, and I redistribute to the poor. The small percentage that is the rich have taken from the larger percentage that is poor. I am balancing the wealth by redistributing it."

"Have you ever asked what is it that makes them poor?" questioned the merchant. "There are two different systems at odds in the land in which we stand: feudalism and capitalism. Feudalism is where the king owns all the land, and he awards certain lands and titles to those who serve him: earls, dukes, barons, lords, and knights. These people manage the lands for the king in exchange for military service and reap all the benefits of the land. The common people do not own the land. They have no individual property rights. They are merely tenants who work the land, cultivate the crops, and have all their productive effort seized by those in power. The people in power are only rich because of their relationship to the king. I am not one of those people. Feudalism is another variation of something known as Fascism. Fascism is when the government does not directly control the means of production but controls the means of distribution. It is Socialism with the veneer of Capitalism."

"What you say is true," Robin Hood acknowledged reluctantly. "But what of the heavy taxes the rich impose on the poor?"

"Who are the rich imposing those heavy taxes and benefiting from them?" replied the merchant. "Those rich people that I have just mentioned are members of the government. To what purpose are those heavy taxes being used? Prince John, who is acting king in King Richard's absence, is collecting taxes to pay mercenaries to overthrow his brother King Richard. That heavy taxation burden by the government and the lack of individual property rights is what causes the people to be poor."

"Well, you are rich just like them, so you must be one and the same," accused Robin Hood.

"As I have said," replied the merchant. "I am not one of those people. I advocate the second system that I previously mentioned, capitalism. I am a capitalist and part of the rightfully rich. I did not gain my fortune because of some relationship to the king. Far from it. I was a commoner who ascended from poverty. I saved what little money I had by denying myself things until I could build capital. With this small amount of capital, I took the risk of purchasing some goods, which I then resold at a profit. I continued this until I could save more capital. I used that capital to invest in businesses run by able individuals such as bakers, blacksmiths, woodworkers, and herdsman. With these businesses, I made a profit. Now that more capital could be amassed, I invested in traders who traveled to faraway lands to bring goods here that were not here before. Each investment I made carried the risk of losing that which I invested. No favors were paid to me. I received no benefit from taxes, yet many people benefit from my undertaken risks. I provide jobs and bring goods to the market. I force no one to buy that which they do not want or need. I do not take from others by force. All of my transactions are voluntarily made by people who will benefit from them."

The merchant continued, "I am a pious man who believes in helping his fellow man. My charity, however, is my choice. I give because I choose to, and my benefit is that I feel good about giving. You cannot force me to give because of some moral standard imposed by others. You rob me of the very benefit of my charity. You take away my good feeling by forcing my hand. Call it taxes, redistribution of wealth, a social safety net, or whatever. You are forcing me into an involuntary transaction—and involuntary transactions are known as theft. You gain my compliance through the tip of your blade. You provide me injury not benefit. Just because your intentions are different, it does not change your means. You and the feudal system that causes these people to be poor are one and the same."

To this, Robin Hood had no response. He stood there for a few moments. Speechless. The old merchant's words sinking in. Finally, he said, "I have never thought of it that way. I guess it seemed easier to blame others than to analyze and identify the true cause. I bid you a good day sir, and safe travels."

As Robin Hood turned to walk away, the old merchant tossed him a bag of gold. "Take it as a donation," smiled the old merchant. "This gold is an individual choice of charity, a voluntary transaction that I have made for which I receive benefit. It is not the product of theft."

Lessons: Regardless of its intent and what name it is given, an involuntary transaction is theft.

Wealth redistribution does not solve the real cause of the poor's predicament. One must take a harder, deeper look at an individual's circumstances and determine the true cause. Is it their own individual, past choices? Or is it a systematized, institutional practice that is preventing their individual advancement? If it is the latter, what is the practice or law?

It is easier to blame external factors that we have no control over. It is harder to identify and examine the individual choices that we do control, because that would require us to take responsibility for the choices that we have made.

Life is a sum of choices. We do not always have the best choices, but we still have choices. One choice will inevitably lead to other choices. The economy is all about choices and the cost of those choices. Resources are limited, including time, focus, and energy. Decisions made to pursue one course of action come at the expense of not being able to utilize those same resources to pursue another course of action.

Sometimes, unknowingly, our cultural norms influence our individual choices. An example of this is consumerism or the need to compare ourselves with another's station in life. This phenomenon must be considered before choices are acted upon. If not, choices can be made that adversely affect one's financial future.

What is the real cause of one's choice? What is the true intent or objective that one wishes to accomplish? Only by being truly honest and accountable with one's self can one be comfortable with the choices that become the sum of one's life.

The Wolf and the Lamb

On a pasture like any other pasture lived a Wolf. The Wolf did not want to feel like an aggressor and reasoned that when he next devoured an animal, he would find a just reason for taking that animal's life to sustain his own. He soon happened to come across a Lamb that had wandered off on his own.

"Are you not going to apologize for the trespass you committed?" accused the Wolf.

"What trespass is that sir?" questioned the Lamb.

"Last year, you came onto my pasture without permission," said the Wolf.

"It could not have been me," explained the Lamb. "I was not yet born last year."

"Well, you came onto my property and drank water from my stream," accused the Wolf.

"I have not yet tasted water," explained the Lamb. "My mother's milk is all that I drink."

"Well, you have eaten grass from my pasture," accused the Wolf. "No permission was given by me."

"It could not have been me," pleaded the Lamb. "I have yet to taste grass. My mother's milk is both my food and drink. It gives me everything I need."

The Wolf, becoming frustrated, grabbed the Lamb and slaughtered him. He devoured the Lamb as quickly as he could.

The only justification that could be found was the ravenous Wolf's own individual need.

Lessons: Tyrants will always rationalize to justify their use of violence. They cannot be reasoned or negotiated with. Logic will not work on those who operate on compulsive necessity because their needs will always supersede the rights and needs of others. Capitalism can only exist when there is a voluntary trade. An exchange that is coerced or taken by force is not a trade; it is theft. Regardless of what it is called: taxes, regulatory fees, or industry-specific licensing fees to conduct business. Involuntary exchange is theft.

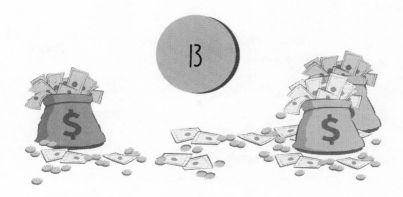

The Scorpion and the Frog

On the bank of a river like any other river lived a Frog. The Frog was kind and often looked for the good in others. He was a happy Frog and spent most of his time lounging in the water and catching flies when he was hungry.

One day, a Scorpion approached him. "Hello Frog," said the Scorpion. "I was hoping that you could take me across the river on your back."

The Frog answered, "I surely cannot do that. Once you are on my back, you will stab me with your stinger. It's just your nature."

"If I were to do that, then I would drown in the river," retorted the Scorpion. "It would not be in my self-interest to stab you with my stinger."

The Frog thought about it and reasoned that the Scorpion was right. It would not be in the Scorpion's self-interest to sting him while he was on his back, regardless of his nature. The Frog agreed to take the Scorpion across the river.

Once they were in the middle of the river, the Scorpion, without warning, stabbed the Frog in the back with his stinger. "You fool," shouted the Frog. "You just killed us both."

"I'm sorry," apologized the Scorpion. "It's just my nature, I can't control it."

Both perished in the depths of the river.

Lessons: Know whom you are dealing with. One's nature should be known before dealing with them. Knowing this, if you continue to deal with them expecting them to act otherwise, you set yourself up for disappointment. This is also true when it comes to who you associate with.

If you associate with negative people, you will also take on their characteristics of negativity. Conversely, if you associate with positive people, you will also take on their characteristics of positivity. This is because a person's character is often displayed by the habits they repeat. We often adapt the habits of those we spend the most time with. Habits are nothing more than learned behavior.

Financially, this is true as well. If you associate yourself with people that have negative financial habits such as: not saving, not budgeting, overspending, taking on bad debt, and not having a financial plan. You will absorb their traits as well. However, if you associate yourself with people that have positive financial habits such as: saving, budgeting, investing, only taking on good debt, and having and adhering to a financial plan. You will absorb their traits as well.

Surround yourself with people that will help you achieve your goals. If you want to accomplish a goal, seek others that have accomplished that goal and seek to learn from them. Individuals learn from experience, but nothing states that you cannot learn from another individual's experiences. This practice will save you time and energy.

People often help those that help themselves. Invest in yourself and you will be surprised at how many will invest in you as well.

Made in the USA
Las Vegas, NV
10 September 2021

30049944R00035